D0274910

EGMONT

We bring stories to life

First published in Great Britain in 2020 by Egmont UK Limited,
2 Minster Court, 10th floor, London EC3R 7BB
www.egmont.co.uk

Written and edited by Catherine Shoolbred
Designed by Jeannette O'Toole for Ruby Shoes Limited

Parental guidance is advised for all craft and colouring activities. Always ask an adult to help when using glue, paint and scissors. Wear protective clothing and cover surfaces to avoid staining.

Stay safe online. Egmont is not responsible for content hosted by third parties.

Egmont takes its responsibility to the planet and its inhabitants very seriously. We aim to use papers from well-managed forests run by responsible suppliers.

ISBN 978 1 4052 9672 4
70858/001
Printed in Italy

....

....

Disney Princess
Annual 2021

Contents

All About ...

Cinderella

Cinderella's mother died when she was young and when her father died too, her unkind stepmother and jealous stepsisters make her work as a servant for them. Her luck changes when she meets her Fairy Godmother, who dresses Cinderella in a beautiful ballgown and glass slippers and sends her to the royal ball in a magical pumpkin coach! She dances for hours with the prince, but has to leave at midnight before the magic runs out. As she rushes away, she leaves behind one glass slipper. Prince Charming is determined to search the whole kingdom to find her.

Prince Charming

He is romantic and loves dancing, so he's the perfect match for Cinderella!

Fairy Godmother

She is sweet and caring and brings love and magic to Cinderella's life.

Gus and Jac

These cute mice will do anything for their best friend Cinderella.

Can you colour Cinderella so she shines like a bright star?

A Party Muddle

4 *So after asking staff and friends to help alongside the Countess' helpers, Cinderella hurried to the mansion.*

5 *Nothing was ready. Cinderella set everyone to work in a flash!*

6 *The mice were in charge of the decorations.*

2 **Count the mice in the picture above.**

Answer on page 69

7 *Cinderella asked some helpers to pick carrots for the cake and pretty flowers she had chosen for the guests. Then she went to the kitchen.*

3 **Join the dots to reveal a flower.**

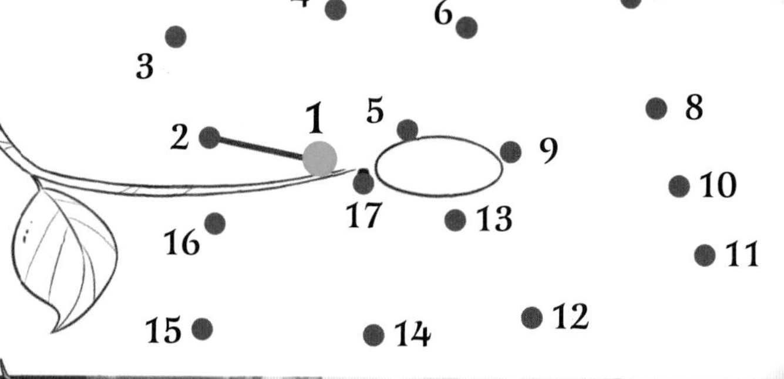

8 *Once she had shown everyone how to make the perfect carrot cake, she left the Prince in charge of the kitchen.*

9 *The Countess booked a magician at short notice. "I've not done magic in a while," he said.*

10 *Before long, the party guests started to arrive.*

11

With the party in full swing, the magician asked for a volunteer to help in his next trick. Cinderella happily joined him on stage.

Wow!

12

At the magic words, a streamer of decorations burst from the magician's hat, much to everyone's surprise!

That's where I put the last streamer!

4

Tick ✔ what appears from the magician's hat.

- ☐ BANANA
- ☐ STREAMER

13

The Countess thanked Cinderella. "This party would have been a disaster without you," she said. "Special things happen when everyone works together," replied Cinderella.

The End

Answers on page 69

Odd One Out

These images of Cinderella look the same, but one is different. Can you spot the odd one out?

Answers on page 69

Shadow Match

Draw lines to match the princesses to their shadows.

A

B

C

D

E

Answers on page 69

All About ...

Moana

Born on the island of Motunui, Moana is the sea-loving headstrong daughter of Chief Tui and Sina. When her island is endangered by a life-killing darkness, Moana is chosen by the ocean to journey beyond the reef and across the sea with Maui, a trickster demigod, to restore the legendary heart of Te Fiti, in order to heal the island and save her people. During her daring adventure, Moana comes to realise that no one can define who you are other than yourself. Ultimately she succeeds in her quest and brings her people and the sea into unity.

Heihei

Moana's pet chicken accidentally goes on Moana's quest with Maui.

Maui

This strong-willed shape-shifting demigod reluctantly helps Moana on her quest.

Sound out these names, then use a pencil or crayon to trace over the letters.

Moana

Maui

Heihei

Te Fiti

Spot the Difference

Moana is enjoying being by the ocean with Gramma Tala and her animal friends.

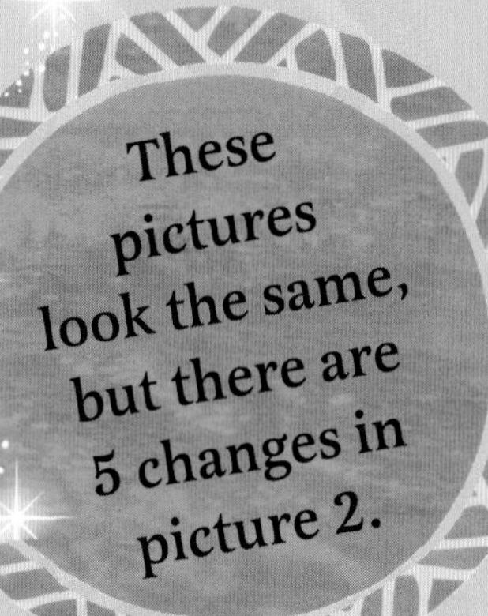

a

b

Answers on page 69

Shell Maze

Moana has found a pretty shell that she's giving to Gramma Tala.

1 Draw a line through the maze to collect the shell, then deliver it to Gramma.

START

FINISH

2 Draw your own shell here.

Answers on page 69

Moana Puzzles

Grab your pencils and help Moana to solve these island puzzles.

1 Match the correct shadow to Moana by drawing a line.

1

2

3

2 Circle what Moana is holding.

a

b

c

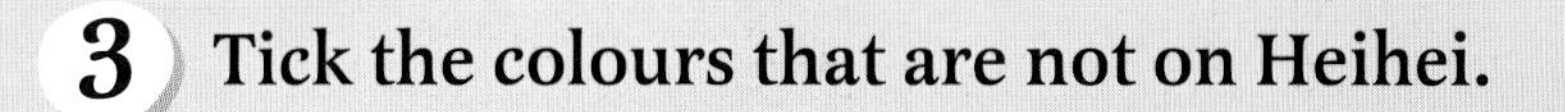

3 Tick the colours that are not on Heihei.

4 Help Gramma Tala match these pretty flowers into pairs.

Answers on page 69

All About ...

Rapunzel

Rapunzel was kidnapped as a baby and raised in a tower by Mother Gothel, who taught her to fear the outside world. Despite her upbringing, Rapunzel is creative, fun-loving, friendly and brave. She also has magical hair that glows when she sings a special song and can heal any ailment including old age. For eighteen years Rapunzel has had one dream: to see the lights that rose into the air every year on her birthday. A chance meeting with Flynn Rider helped to make that dream come true.

Mother Gothel

She's selfish and vain. She uses the power of Rapunzel's hair to keep her young.

Flynn Rider (Eugene Fitzherbert)

Eugene, also known as Flynn Rider, is a notorious thief known for his charm and quick-wit.

Pascal

This cute chameleon mimes, makes noises and changes colour to communicate with Rapunzel.

Use the small picture
as a guide to help you
colour in Rapunzel.

Snowy Wonderland

1 *One morning, Rapunzel and Pascal woke up to a great surprise. "It's snowed overnight!" said Rapunzel excitedly. Anything that made her day in the tower a little different made her happy. A snowy day was her favourite kind of different day.*

2 *Rapunzel rushed to the windowsill with Pascal. It was a pretty snowy wonderland outside and all the forest creatures were having fun in the snow!*

1

Tick the animals you can spot on this page.

a ☐ b ☐ c ☐ d ☐

3

Pascal looked down longingly. "Oh Pascal, you'd like to run down the tower and play wouldn't you?" said Rapunzel. Pascal wanted to go down and join the other animals - but not without Rapunzel.

4

"Well, if you prefer, we can curl up in front of the fire and read a book." said Rapunzel. And that's just what they did. The warmth from the fire made Pascal sleepy.

a b c d

2 **Circle the pictures with green in them.**

5

While Pascal slept, Rapunzel started thinking about how fun it would be for Pascal to play in the snow. Then she had a great idea!

6

She would build a snowy wonderland for him! First she made a small mountain by piling up the snow. The ice underneath the snow made a perfect ice-skating rink!

Answers on page 69

7

Next, Rapunzel made a snowman and a sledge. Then she worked on a pair of tiny ice-skates. She could hardly wait to see Pascal's face when he saw it.

8

When Pascal woke up, he was thrilled by it. He couldn't wait to play in the snowy playground that Rapunzel had made just for him.

3 How did Pascal feel? Circle the right answer.

a b c d

9

Pascal put on the skates and soon he was gliding across the ice faster and faster. "Fantastic!" cried Rapunzel. "You're really ice-skating!"

10

Then Pascal had fun sledging down the snowy mountain!

11

Rapunzel was too big to play in the snowy wonderland, but watching her best friend have so much fun was a truly wonderful feeling.

4 Spot these details in the big picture.

The End

5 Trace the letters and see what Rapunzel used to build the special wonderland.

snow

Answers on page 69

Sudoku

Draw in the missing shapes to help Rapunzel complete the grid.

Each row needs to have 3 different shapes in it.

Answers on page 69

Pick a Princess

Follow the instructions below to find out which Princess you are most like.

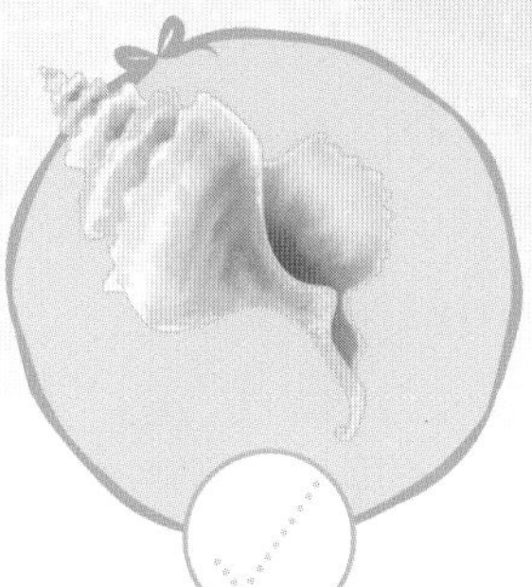

Tick ✔ your 5 favourite pictures. Then match the colour you picked most often to the princesses below.

Mostly green

Like Ariel you are fun and love adventures. Colour in the gem.

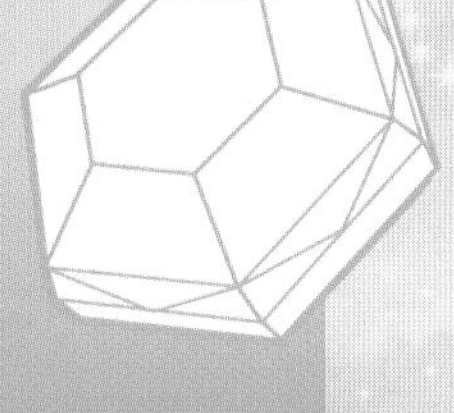

Mostly purple

Like Aurora you are kind and caring. Colour in the flower.

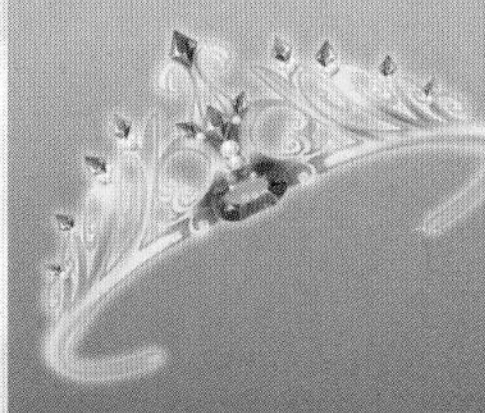

Mostly blue

Like Cinderella you are loyal and helpful. Colour in the star.

All About ...

Belle

Despite her beauty and kindness, Belle has always been an outsider due to her love of reading and her eccentric inventor father. She wants adventure and dreams of something bigger than life in her small town. She is sure of one thing, she does not want to marry Gaston, no matter how hard he tries to change her mind. She stands up for herself and looks past the surface to see the best in people, even the seemingly horrible Beast.

Beast

At first glance he is just what his name implies, a beast, but Belle brings out the very best in him.

Gaston

This arrogant hunter believes women shouldn't read as they should focus on flattering him instead!

Lumiere and Cogsworth

The enchanted objects help the Beast find love and break the curse so they can all be human again.

Belle's favourite place is the Beast's library. Sound out these words to learn something about Belle, then trace over the letters with a pencil or crayon.

Belle
loves to
read

A Helpful Plan

Oh no! It's so muddy.

1 Belle was excited because it was the day of the village's outdoor fair, which she'd helped to organise. But when she opened her curtains, she saw there had been heavy rain overnight.

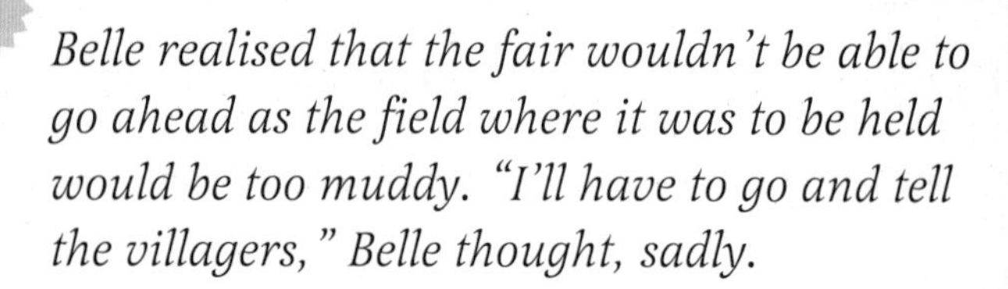

2 Belle realised that the fair wouldn't be able to go ahead as the field where it was to be held would be too muddy. "I'll have to go and tell the villagers," Belle thought, sadly.

I have a plan, Philippe!

3 Before she headed into the village, Belle went to feed her horse, Philippe. Seeing him munch on his hay gave her an idea. "Maybe we can have the fair after all," she thought.

Answers on page 69

To the fair, Philippe.
4
When Philippe had finished his breakfast, Belle harnessed him up and set off to a nearby farm. The kind farmer gave Belle a cartload of hay to lay over the muddy field.
2
Write over the first letter when you spot each animal in the picture above.
Sheep
Cow
5
When she got to the village, Belle was shocked to see an upturned apple cart blocking the road. "Are you OK?" she asked the cart owner. Luckily he was.
I can't thank you enough.
6
Belle rushed to the village to get help, then she and the villagers heaved the cart back onto its wheels. "Take these," the grateful cart owner said, handing Belle a huge sack of apples.

At the field where the fair was to be held, Belle quickly covered the muddy patches with hay. "It's not as bad as I thought it would be," she said, noticing the pile of leftover hay.

Just then, Belle remembered a game she loved playing when she went to fairs with her father as a child. "I've got everything I need to make my own game," she thought, happily.

Belle built small haystacks with the leftover hay and hid the apples inside. When the fair opened, the children loved finding the apples and sharing them with Philippe.

3 **Count the apples and write over the dotty number.**

11

10

At the end of the fair, prizes were given out to the winners of each event. Belle was delighted when she and Philippe were awarded a special rosette for being the most helpful team.

11

"I couldn't have done it without you," she told her horse as she proudly attached the rosette to his reins. "Let's have an apple to celebrate!"

The End

Spot the small details in the big picture above.

5 **Colour this rosette for Belle and Philippe.**

Answers on page 69

Starlight Dance

The enchanted objects are happy to see Belle and the Beast enjoying their dance together.

Colour in a rose every time you spot a difference between these pictures. There are 6 to find.

Answers on page 69

© Disney
Be your own
HERO!
CUT HERE

CUT HERE

Which is your FAVOURITE *Princess?*

Be a Princess

These princesses rule! Now it's time for you to be a princess, too.

Draw yourself as a princess here, then tick ✔ all the words that describe you.

independent

optimistic

brave

creative

cheerful

fearless

adventurous

kind

determined

All About ...

Aurora

Princess Aurora is beautiful and graceful. As a child she was cursed by Maleficent, so to keep her safe, her father sent her to live in the woods as Briar Rose. She was raised by the good fairies Flora, Fauna and Merryweather. A chance meeting with Prince Phillip causes her to throw caution to the wind and her peaceful life changes when she learns the truth of her birth.

Prince Phillip

He falls in love with Aurora believing she is a peasant girl. He takes on Maleficent to save his true love.

Flora, Fauna and Merryweather

The good fairies disguised themselves as peasants to protect Aurora from Maleficent.

WHAT COMES NEXT?

Can you work out who comes next in each sequence?

Answers on page 69

True or False?

Aurora is warming up beside a roaring fire after being outside picking flowers.

1

Look at the picture as you count to 10. Then cover it up.

2

Answer the questions. Tick ✔ for true and cross ✘ for false.

1 *The fire is keeping Aurora warm.*

TRUE

FALSE

2 *Aurora is wearing a blue dress.*

TRUE

FALSE

3 *The cushion on the bed is yellow.*

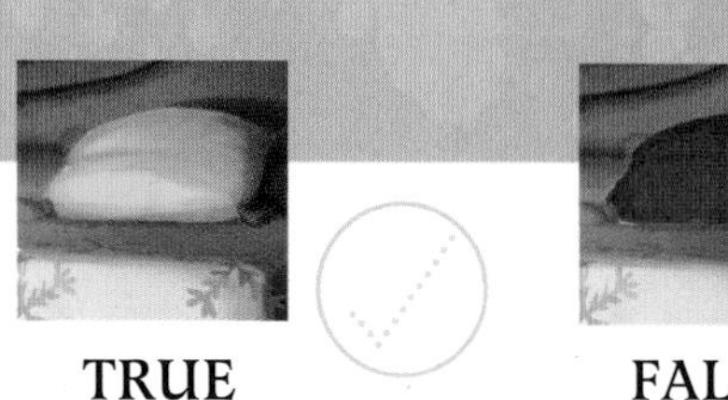

TRUE

FALSE

Answers on page 69

Picture Story

Read this story using the pictures to help you.

Maleficent

Prince Phillip

didn't grow up as a princess. the evil fairy cursed her, so 's father sent her to live in the woods as a peasant. The good fairies taught to love nature and music. One day, heard singing and rushed to meet her. When finds out she's a princess, she returns to the castle. But falls victim to

's evil spell. needs 's help to end the evil curse.

The End

Aurora's Flowers

Each of the 3 good fairies has picked a special flower for Aurora.

1

Draw a line from each fairy flower through the maze to Aurora.

FINISH

2

Follow the lines to match up the picture to the flower name.

a

b

c

daisy

rose

3

Write over the dotty letters.

4

Colour the vase Aurora has used for the flowers from the fairies.

All About ...

Jasmine

She leads a luxurious life as daughter of the Sultan and princess of Agrabah, but Jasmine is lonely. Her only companions are her father and her pet tiger, Rajah. She longs to see the world, but she's forbidden from leaving the palace. She is fiercely independent and incredibly compassionate. She wants to do right by her kingdom and her subjects and gets to learn more about them and herself when she meets Aladdin.

Aladdin

His world is turned upside down when he's tricked into stealing a magic lamp.

The Genie

He's one of the most powerful beings in the universe who can shape-shift into almost anything.

Jafar

This evil sorcerer wants to be the most powerful Genie in the universe.

Answers on page 69

Jasmine Jigsaw

Jasmine loves hanging out with her friends!

1

2

3

4

a

b

c

d

Match the jigsaw pieces to the spaces in the picture.

Answers on page 69

Words about Jasmine

Trace the letters to read these words that describe Jasmine.

All About ...

Ariel

The youngest daughter of King Triton loves music, exploring and the human world. Her father orders her to never go to the ocean surface, but she can't help herself. Her life is turned upside down when she rescues Prince Eric, a human, from a shipwreck and falls in love with him. She makes a deal with Ursula, the sea witch, trading her voice for the chance to be human for three days. Things do not go as planned – she should have known better than to trust a sea witch!

King Triton

He's furious when Ariel disobeys him and meets Prince Eric, but he sacrifices himself to save her.

Ursula

She sees Ariel's love for Prince Eric as her chance to gain power over the seas.

Prince Eric

Prince Eric easily falls under Ursula's spell, but true love ultimately wins out.

DOT-TO-DOT FLOUNDER

Join the dots to complete the picture of Ariel's friend, Flounder, then colour him in.

Happy to be a Mermaid

1 One sunny day, Ariel watched a human family on the beach. The two young girls let the gentle waves chase them up and down the shore, while their parents watched. "How wonderful it must be to have legs to run with," sighed Ariel, "and feet to leave footprints in the sand."

1

Follow the path and discover something beautiful.

2 "Ariel! What are you doing?" scolded Sebastian as he climbed up onto the rock. "Hi Sebastian!" said Ariel. "I'm just wishing I could run and jump like those children."

3 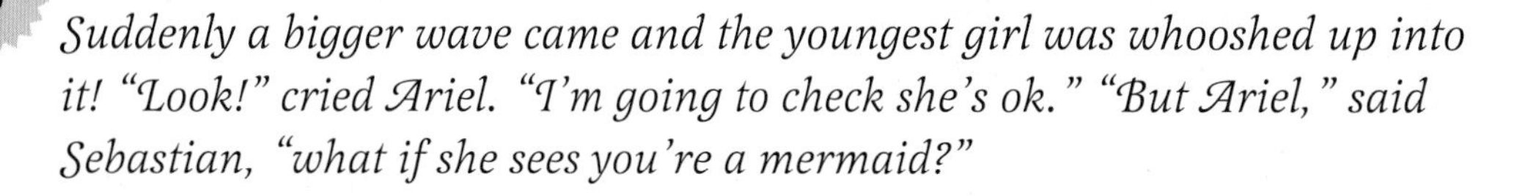

Suddenly a bigger wave came and the youngest girl was whooshed up into it! "Look!" cried Ariel. "I'm going to check she's ok." "But Ariel," said Sebastian, "what if she sees you're a mermaid?"

4

Ariel didn't listen and dived into the sea. From beneath the water she lifted the girl to the surface, away from the big wave.

5

Ariel quickly sat the little girl down on the rock, just as her family came running towards her. They were glad to see that she was safe and happy.

6

"You nearly got caught!" scolded Sebastian, but Ariel could see he was not really angry this time.

2

Circle who Ariel helped.

a

b

c

d

Answers on page 69

7

The next day, Ariel wanted to return to the rock. "But why?" asked Sebastian. "If I can't run and jump myself, at least I can enjoy watching someone else do it," said Ariel.

8

But when they arrived, the beach was empty. "Come now," said Sebastian. "Let's go back home." "But look, Sebastian!" said Ariel. She picked up a bottle with a piece of paper rolled up inside it.

9

*Ariel pulled the paper out and unrolled it. It was a beautiful drawing of a mermaid. On the back, the little girl had written: "***I wish I could swim like a mermaid!***"*

3

Draw a picture that you would like to put in the bottle for Ariel.

10

"She's right," smiled Ariel. "I am lucky!" And with that she flipped her tail fins and twirled in the ocean as only a mermaid could!

Being a mermaid is amazing!

Eh ... being a crab isn't so bad, either!

The End

4

How many seahorses can you count in the picture above?

5

Help Ariel find her way home to the palace.

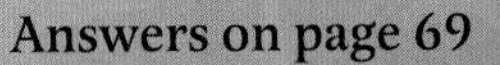
Answers on page 69

Sunken Ship

Ariel and Flounder have discovered a shipwreck at the bottom of the sea.

1

Can you find these things in the big picture? Tick ✔ the boxes as you do.

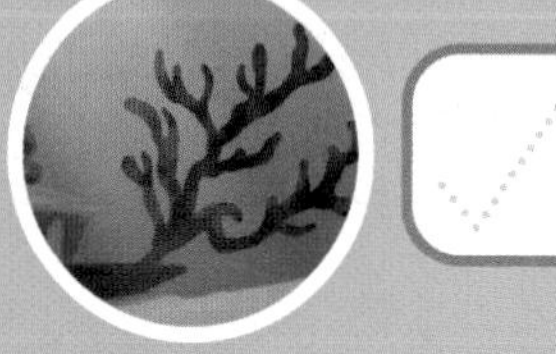

2

Draw a line through the ship for Flounder to get to Ariel.

3
How many stripes
does this fish have?
Trace over the
right number.
2
or
3
Answers on page 69
4
Colour in
the fish.

All About ...

Snow White

Snow White is best known for her kindness to all living creatures. She is forced to flee the castle when the Queen, her wicked stepmother, plans to kill her. She runs away to the forest and makes a happy home with her new friends, the Seven Dwarfs. The Queen tricks Snow White into eating a poisoned apple, but luckily it just puts her into an enchanted sleep. She is woken from her deathly slumber by a charming prince.

Wicked Queen

She asks the Magic Mirror who is the fairest in the land. When it says Snow White, she tries to kill her.

Seven Dwarfs

Snow White lives happily with the Seven Dwarfs: Sleepy, Grumpy, Doc, Dopey, Bashful, Sneezy and Happy.

The Prince

He falls in love with Snow White's singing before they even meet. He saves her with Love's First Kiss.

Help Snow White find her way through the maze to Dopey.

Circle the animals you pass in the maze.

a

b

c

d

Answers on page 69

The Castle Ghost

1

The Seven Dwarfs were excited to be staying overnight at Snow White's castle. "Why, I see you've brought your own pillow, Happy," said Snow White. "It makes me feel at home," he replied, cheerfully.

1

How many Dwarfs are looking at the picture?

3

2

The Dwarfs put their things down and admired their surroundings. "Let me show you around before dinner," said Snow White.

3

After dinner, Snow White noticed that the Dwarfs were looking sleepy. She showed them to their beds and said goodnight. They were so tired, they didn't even ask for a bedtime story!

4

But no sooner had the Dwarfs fallen asleep, when a loud noise woke them all up. "Don't worry, it's just a door banging the wind shut. Erm? I mean, the wind banging the door shut," stammered Doc.

2

Circle the Dwarf missing from the picture.

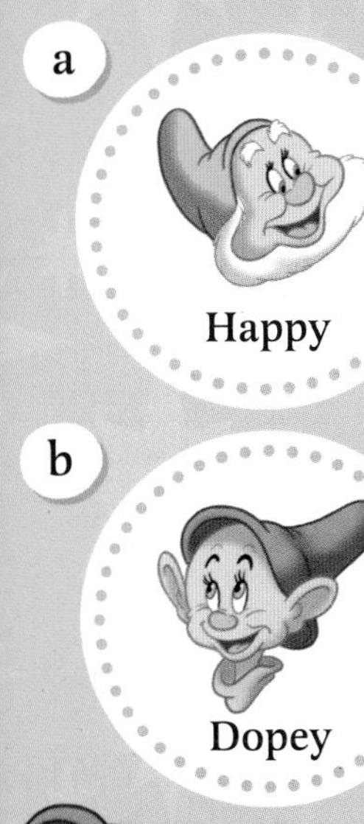

Found you!

5

Suddenly a ghost appeared! Terrified, the Dwarfs all huddled together. "Ah-ha! Found you," echoed a voice.

6

"Where's Happy?" yawned Sleepy, noticing he was missing. "The ghost must have taken him," replied Grumpy. The six Dwarfs went to find Snow White to tell her.

Answers on page 69

7

They found Snow White by the kitchen. "A ghost captured Happy!" cried Grumpy. "Why, Happy is right here," said a puzzled Snow White.

And there aren't any ghosts in the castle.

8

But we heard ***"THUD! THUD! THUD!"*** *said Doc. "And then the ghost said '****Aaa-AH-HA!*** *Found you,'" jittered Sneezy. Dopey nodded his head in agreement so quickly, it looked like it might fall off!*

3

Point to Grumpy.

I'm telling you ... we saw a ghost!

9

"Oh my!" chuckled Snow White. "It was Happy you heard. He had forgotten his pillow and went to get it. His voice must have echoed through the castle when he found it.

10

"But we definitely SAW a ghost!" insisted Grumpy. "Yep, we sure did see a ghost," said Doc. "Right by the window, so it was."

11

"Why don't we go and look?" said Snow White. She led her guests back to the bedroom.

4

Finish colouring the curtain.

12

Sure enough, there appeared to be a ghost in front of the open window. "See! There's the ghost!" said Grumpy, pointing to it. Snow White went to the window and closed it.

13

"It's only a curtain flapping in the wind," she said.

14

"Well how about that!" said Doc. All the Dwarfs were relieved and now wide awake.

15

"I'll read you a story to help you go to sleep," said Snow White. "As long as it's not a ghost story," said Bashful. Everyone laughed, even Grumpy!

The End

All About ...

Mulan

When her aging father is ordered to serve in the Imperial army, Mulan cuts off her hair and disguises herself as a man to go in his place. She fights bravely but her lie is revealed and she's released from service. She sees a threat coming and warns her commander, Li Shang, even though he no longer wishes to speak to her. She also devises a plan to save the Emperor from Shan-Yu, defeating the villain once and for all.

Li Shang

The captain trains new recruits, like Mulan. He is angry about her deception, but helps her to save the Emperor.

The Emperor

When he's rescued from Shan-Yu, he recognises Mulan's bravery and bows to her, showing her respect and honour.

Can you match Mulan's animal friends to the close-ups of them in the circles?

1

2

3

4

a

b

c

d

Answers on page 69

Steps to Success

One day, Shang arrived with some super news. "We have been invited to the Emperor's annual dance," he told Mulan.

"How wonderful," Mulan said.

An invite to the Emperor's annual dance was a very special honour – but Mulan would have to learn the dance steps first.

Grandmother Fa tried to show her. But Mulan – who was a graceful warrior – was so nervous that she tripped over her own feet and ended up on the floor!

When her father tried to dance with her, Mulan trod on his toes so many times that he had to go and lie down!

"I'll never be able to dance well," Mulan complained to Mushu.

"Of course you will," Mushu told her. "Just don't try so hard."

Mulan didn't know how to do that, but Mushu had a plan. "We'll do something you are good at – practising with your sword," he said.

"And, while you're doing that, I'll show you the steps."

Circle who helped Mulan learn to dance.

Answers on page 69

So, that afternoon, while Mulan carefully practised her sword moves, Mushu taught her how to dance. When she lifted her sword, he lifted his left foot – and she copied him. When she lowered her sword, Mushu did a twirl – and Mulan twirled, too.

Before long, every movement of Mulan's sword seemed to come with a dance step! When the sword was taken out of her hands, Mulan found she could dance beautifully without even thinking about it. Mushu's clever plan had worked!

Mulan and Shang were the favourites at the Emperor's Dance, and they were praised for their gracefulness and beauty.

"How did you learn to dance so well, Mulan?" Shang asked her.

"It was a fight at first," Mulan admitted, "but I just kept trying until I got it right."

Shang nodded. "That's just like you, Mulan," he told her. "You never give up on anything."

The End

Flower Fan

ASK A GROWN-UP FOR HELP.

Make your own flower fan so you can stay as cool as Mulan!

YOU WILL NEED:

- paper plate
- glitter pens
- paper
- sticky tape
- craft glue
- safety scissors
- a clean stick
- sequins

1 Cut out the middle of a paper plate. Tape a piece of plain paper to the back of the paper plate frame. Draw flowers on the paper with glitter pens and leave to dry.

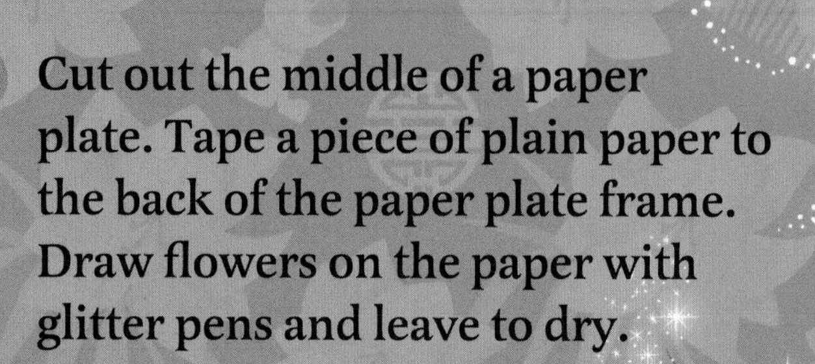

b

c

2 Decorate the stick and attach it to the back of your paper frame. To finish your fan, glue sequins around the rim. Now you have your own fan to play with.

a

Spot Cri-Kee's correct shadow on the page.

Answers on page 69

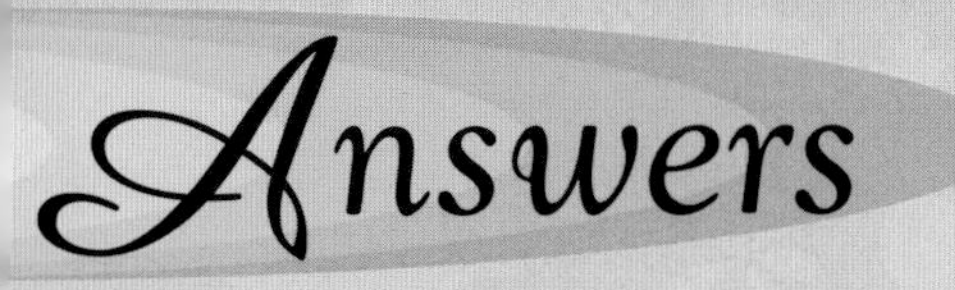

Answers

PAGE 11 *A Party Muddle*
2. There are 5 mice
4. A streamer

PAGE 14 *Odd One Out*
Picture 5 is the right answer

PAGE 15 *Shadow Match*
1 – D, 2 – E, 3 – C, 4 – A, 5 – B

PAGE 18 *Spot the Difference*

PAGE 19 *Shell Maze*

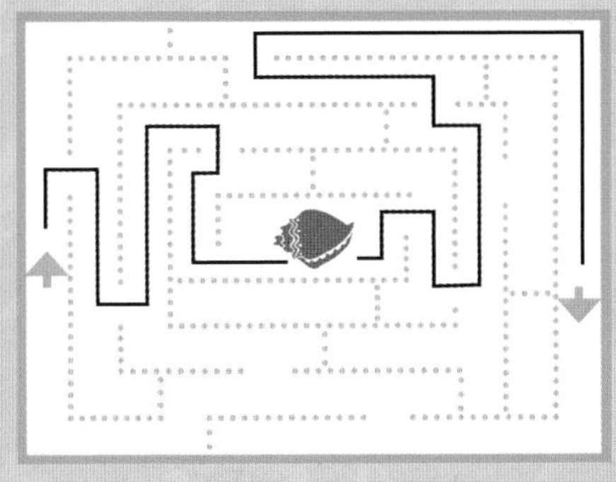

PAGE 20 *Moana Puzzles*
1. Shadow 3
2. c – oar
3. e and f
4.

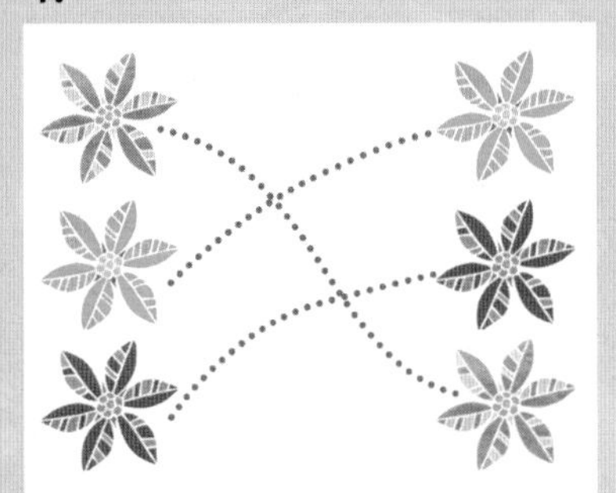

PAGE 24 *Snowy Wonderland*
1. Animal d isn't on the page
2. a, b and c
3. Picture b

PAGE 28 *Sudoku*

PAGE 32 *A Helpful Plan*
1. Hay 3. 11 apples
4.

PAGE 36 *Starlight Dance*

PAGE 41 *What Comes Next*

PAGE 42 *True or False?*
1. True 2. False 3. True

PAGE 44 *Aurora's Flowers*
1.

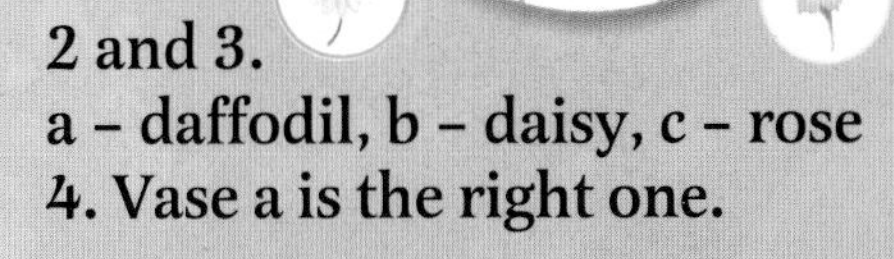

2 and 3.
a – daffodil, b – daisy, c – rose
4. Vase a is the right one.

PAGE 47 *All About Jasmine*
2. Shadow a

PAGE 48 *Jasmine Jigsaw*
1 – d, 2 – a, 3 – c, 4 – b

PAGE 53 *Happy to be a Mermaid*
2. Picture b
4. There are 6 seahorses
5.

PAGE 56 *Sunken Ship*
1.

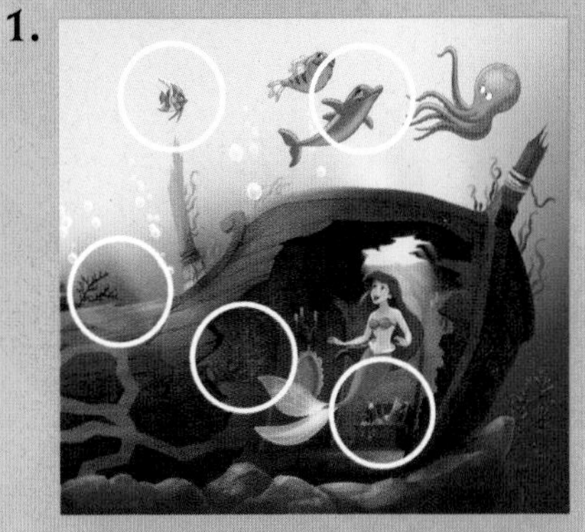

2.

3. The fish has 3 stripes

PAGE 58 *All About Snow White*

You pass b, c and d in the maze

PAGE 60 *The Castle Ghost*
1. There are 3 dwarfs
2. Happy is missing

PAGE 65 *All About Mulan*
1 – c, 2 – a, 3 – d, 4 – b

PAGE 66 *Steps to Success*
Mushu helped Mulan to dance

PAGE 68 *Flower Fan*
Shadow c